A Boy Hears About Jesus

A Boy Hears About Jesus

BY EDITH FRASER

illustrated by Kurt Werth

ABINGDON PRESS

NEW YORK   NASHVILLE

First published in Great Britain under the
title DAVID JOHN HEARS ABOUT JESUS.

Copyright © 1961, 1965 Abingdon Press.
Printed in the United States of America. Library
of Congress Catalog Card Number: 65-10720.

Contents

A Boy Hears About Jesus

THE TIRED DONKEY

"Away in a manger, no crib for a bed," sang Susan, as she mixed some bright red for the holly on the Christmas card she was painting.

"What's a manger?" asked David John, making a yellow loop for a long paper chain. It looked splendid, although there seemed to be rather a lot of glue on it.

"A manger? Why, it's a feeding-trough for the animals," answered Susan, and leaned back to admire her holly.

"But what animals?" asked her brother, frowning at his sticky fingers.

"Come and look!" said Mother, and spread a big picture on the table. David John saw a stable, full of animals and people. In the middle was a lady in blue, smiling down at a baby.

"Why, it's the baby Jesus!" cried Susan. "Let's cut out the animals and things and make a model!"

"That's a good idea!" said Mother. "We'll paste it on some cardboard so that the animals will stand up straight."

"I'll get the scissors," said Susan.

"And I've got the glue—lots of it," added David John. "I'll cut out the donkey first."

"Then I'll do the manger," suggested Susan.

Soon they were busy cutting round all the edges, which, with donkeys, was very hard, thought David John, snipping carefully between two long ears.

"There! Look at my donkey!" he cried. "What was he doing in the stable?"

"Tell us that story again, Mother," begged Susan. So, while she cut a cardboard prop to make the donkey stand up, Mother began.

"The donkey lived in Nazareth, for he belonged to Joseph the carpenter and his young wife Mary. One day they all set out on a long, long journey to Bethlehem. It was a rough, hilly road, and the donkey, who was carrying Mary, began to feel very tired. But Joseph trudged along beside him, and Mary spoke gently to him, so he tried not to stumble on the dusty roads.

"At last they saw Bethlehem in the distance, and the donkey began to look forward to his supper. But by now the road was crowded with many other people, all going to Bethlehem, some on camels, some on donkeys, and the rest walking. The narrow streets of the little town were full of hurrying, jostling crowds, and the donkey was glad that Joseph was there to lead him to the inn where they were to sleep. When they reached the courtyard, the donkey sighed

anxiously, for it was already crowded with animals, people, and children, all tired, hungry, and irritable. The innkeeper came bustling by. 'There is no room for you here,' he frowned."

"Oh, the poor donkey!" interrupted David John.

"Sh!" said Susan, cutting round a nanny goat's horns. "Go on, Mother."

"When the innkeeper saw how tired they were," her

mother continued, "he thought for a moment. 'There's the stable—' he suggested doubtfully. Then Mary smiled, and the donkey pricked up his ears as the innkeeper opened the heavy door. The stable wasn't much of a place, but there was plenty of clean straw, and a little lamp that made a warm glow."

"Look, there it is! Doesn't it look cozy!" murmured Susan, gazing at the picture.

"Now tell about the animals," said David John.

"Well, they made room for the tired donkey, who was soon enjoying his supper," said Mother. "When Joseph had closed the door, and shut out the noise from the crowded courtyard, it was very quiet in the stable. And there, among the friendly animals, the baby Jesus was born. Mary had no cradle for her baby, so she laid him in the manger, full of sweet-scented hay."

"That was a good idea," smiled David John, "and it was all right, because the animals had finished their

12

supper." Then he pointed to the picture. "Look!" he added. "I can see a big star shining down on the stable."

"Some shepherds, guarding their sheep on the hills near Bethlehem, saw that star, too," his mother went on. "And as they looked up, suddenly a bright angel came to tell them about the newborn Jesus, the Son of God."

"And it's all in the carol, Mother!" cried Susan eagerly, and began to sing, "While shepherds watched their flocks by night." David John joined in, but when he had sung all the words he knew, he stopped.

"Go on with the story, Mother," he said, wondering whether the sheep had felt frightened of the angel.

"As soon as the angel had told the shepherds where to find the baby Jesus, a host of other angels appeared in the sky, singing for joy because the Son of God was born," Mother continued.

"I know! Hark the herald angels sing," nodded Susan.

"Tell about the star, Mother," begged David John.

"The shepherds stared at each other in amazement. But there shone the star, right above the sleeping town. Without a word they ran into Bethlehem, the slap-slap of their sandals echoing through the quiet streets. When they reached the yard of the inn, they stopped. There was no newborn baby here. Suddenly they noticed a faint streak of light coming from under a doorway, and, over it, the star shone down. Very quietly they opened the door, and tiptoed into the stable. There in the manger, just as the angel had told them, lay the baby Jesus."

"Didn't he wake up and cry?" asked David John.

13

"The animals stirred when they heard the shepherd's excited voices," said Mother, "but the baby did not cry."

Very quietly, Susan began to sing.

> *The stars in the bright sky looked down where He lay,*
> *The little Lord Jesus asleep in the hay,*

then Mother joined in.

> *The cattle are lowing, the Baby awakes,*
> *But little Lord Jesus, no crying He makes.*

Suddenly David John remembered the next bit.

> *I love Thee, Lord Jesus! Look down from the sky,*
> *And stay by my side until morning is nigh,*

they all sang together.

"And very well sung too!" said another voice.

David John looked up. There stood his father.

"Oh, Daddy!" cried Susan. "We've all forgotten the time, because Mother has been telling us the Christmas story."

"I like that story," added David John slowly. As his father switched on the light, he looked at the model. There they all were, the oxen, the goat, the donkey, Joseph and Mary, and the baby Jesus asleep in the manger. The shepherds were there, too, and one was carrying a little lamb in his arms, and the bright star shone down.

"Can my donkey see the baby from where he's standing?" asked David John.

"I'm sure he can," answered Susan.

"It's a beautiful story, isn't it?" smiled David John.

"The best in the world," said Mother.

THE STRANGE VISITORS

So THEY had supper, and David John and Susan made the salad, which was a nice job. Afterward they played with Tommy, their cat, but in no time at all, Mother said it was bedtime for David John.

As he climbed slowly up the stairs, David John saw the stars through the window, and he remembered.

"Mother, was the Christmas star as bright as those stars?" he asked.

"Much brighter," answered Mother.

"It must have shone a long way, then," said the boy.

"It shone so brightly that people in other countries saw it too," his mother added. "Wise men, who lived far away in the East, saw the wonderful new star, and felt sure that some mighty king had been born."

"So what did they do?" demanded David John as he kicked off his socks and jumped into the bathtub.

"Well, what did the shepherds do?" asked Mother.

David John thought for a moment as he splashed about.

"Goodness! Did those wise men go to see the baby, too?" he exclaimed. "How did they know which way to go?"

"Why, they saw the star," said Mother, "so they set out to travel toward the place over which it shone."

"Go on, Mother," begged David John. So, while he scrubbed his knees, his mother told him the story.

"Day after day, night after night, the wise men swayed along on their tall camels, over hills and through valleys," she said. "They crossed deserts, waded through swift rivers, and traveled on and on until at last they reached Jerusalem. There they reined in their camels and called down to the citizens hurrying by. 'Where is he that is born King of the Jews?' they cried. The people stared up in surprise at the strange visitors, and shrugged their shoulders. They had not heard of any newborn king. Cruel King Herod had no baby son, that was certain. 'We know of no newborn king,' they muttered, and hurried away to tell the king about the strange travelers."

"Was the king pleased?" frowned David John.

"No, he was *not!*" answered Mother. "Herod himself, not some unknown baby, was the king of the Jews, and king he meant to be. This child must be destroyed, and quickly."

"But how was he going to find the baby?" wondered David John.

"Ah! He had a very clever idea," his mother went on. "He would let the visitors do that for him! So he sent for them secretly, and pretended to welcome them. 'Go,' he said, 'and search for this newborn king. When you have found him, come and tell me, so that I, too, may greet him.'

18

And the wise men, bowing low before Herod, did not see his cruel smile."

David John frowned anxiously, but his mother continued.

"In the palace yard, lighted by the servants' flaring torches, the travelers mounted their kneeling camels and rode away. And the bright star seemed always before them as they journed along the quiet road to Bethlehem. There, in the little town, they saw no royal palace, no splendid mansion, only the star silvering the roof of a small house from which a faint light shone. When the wise men opened the door, they knew that they had come to the end of their strange journey. For there in the glow of the small clay lamp they saw the king."

"And it was the baby Jesus," whispered David John.

His mother nodded and went on.

"Without a word, the travelers fell on their knees and bowed their heads before the little child, while his mother watched in silent wonder. But she said nothing as

the visitors opened their treasures, and gave him three precious gifts—gold, frankincense, and myrrh."

"They don't sound much like presents for a *baby*," murmured David John doubtfully.

"That was what his mother thought at first," Mother agreed, "but then she understood. Royal gold, that was a gift for a king—and her baby would be the greatest king of all. Frankincense, that smelled so sweet burning on the

Temple altars, that was for a priest—and no priest would be as holy as her child. And myrrh, that was for those in pain—and even she could not save her son from pain. At last the wise men turned away from the quiet room, their eyes shining with wonder and joy, and went out to their waiting camels."

"Did they go back and tell King Herod?" asked David John.

"No, because God warned them in a dream of Herod's cruel plan," answered Mother. "So they hurried away from Jerusalem, and went back to their own country by a different road."

David John gave a sigh of relief. Then, as his mother rubbed him dry in the big towel, Susan came in to say good night. David John began to tell Susan about the travelers, the journey, and the shining star, and she ran into her bedroom and came back with a picture book.

"Look," she said, "there are the three kings!" There they were in the picture, kneeling down and holding up their presents for the baby to see. But David John was puzzled.

"Kings?" he muttered. "Mother didn't say they were kings."

"Well, nobody really knows," Mother agreed, "but in the old days people used to think they were, and so that's how they are generally drawn in the pictures."

"It's in the carol, too," added Susan, and began to sing:

We three kings of orient are!
Bearing gifts we travel afar,

21

and, when she came to the chorus, Mother and David John joined in:

Star of wonder, star of light,
Star with royal beauty bright,
Westward leading still proceeding,
Guide us with thy heavenly light.

David John enjoyed singing that tune. It sounded just like the camels plodding on and on across the desert, and he could almost see the great star shining. But suddenly he remembered the other king.

"What about King Herod?" he asked.

"King Herod waited and waited for the wise men to come back," said his mother, "but at last he realized that he had been tricked. Then he was angry—terribly angry. This baby must be destroyed, and there was only one way to make sure. So he ordered his soldiers to kill every baby boy in Bethlehem."

"Oh, *no!*" gasped David John. "But what about Jesus?"

"That very night," went on Mother, "God sent a messenger to Joseph in a dream."

"Go on, Mother," said David John impatiently. "What did the angel say?"

"He said, 'Get up, Joseph! Take the child and his mother and flee to Egypt. Stay there until I tell you it is safe to return, for Herod is searching for the child to kill him.' So Joseph woke Mary and told her the angel's message, then hurried out to harness the sleepy donkey, while she packed up their things, very quietly, so as not to wake the baby."

David John chuckled. "I expect that donkey was surprised!"

"And more still when Mary, holding the sleeping child close, was lifted onto his back, and they set out in the darkness. He couldn't understand why Joseph led him through such narrow alleys, by such rough tracks and along such hidden paths. On they went, swiftly and secretly, hour after hour, until the donkey was very tired indeed. Although he tried not to stumble, he couldn't think why Joseph, who was in such a hurry, wasn't traveling on the proper roads."

"I know why!" cried David John, scrambling into his pajamas. "It was to dodge the soldiers."

"That's right," smiled Mother. "But, for all that, Joseph knew that the baby would never be safe in Herod's

land. So on they went, day after day. Mary was tired and homesick for her own little house in Nazareth, and Joseph was worried about finding work in a foreign land. As for the donkey, his head drooped with weariness. But at last they came to Egypt, where no king would harm the child, and there they could rest in peace.''

"The donkey must have been glad,'' smiled David John.

"So were Joseph and Mary,'' his mother added. "It must have been hard for a carpenter without his tools to earn a living in an unknown land, and for a Jewish girl to make a home among darkskinned strangers who spoke a foreign language. But the baby was safe, and somehow they managed. And there, in Egypt, the little Jesus began to grow up.''

"Like Patsy Jane's baby brother?'' asked David John.

"Just the same,'' Mother agreed. "He cut his first teeth, started to crawl, said a few little words, and tried to walk—.''

"And fell over sometimes?'' interrupted David John.

"Like any other little boy,'' Mother said. David John was very quiet as he brushed his teeth, said his prayers, and jumped into bed. When Mother had tucked him in, he thought of something else.

"Do you think his mother kissed him good night, too?'' he asked slowly.

"I'm sure she did,'' smiled Mother, as she put out the light.

"That's good,'' said David John, and snuggled down to sleep.

THE BOY JESUS

"Look, Mother! Daddy and I have made you a fine new kitchen shelf," shouted David John.

"It'll be better still when we've planed off the rough edges," said his father. So David John stood very still and watched as the plane hissed along the shelf, then growled at the knotty bit in the corner. As he watched, out curved the most beautiful shaving, long and silky, shining and golden, and light as a feather.

"Look at that!" beamed David John, as he twisted it round his finger, then ran to show his mother.

"Now watch!" he said, and pulled the shaving out straight. Then suddenly he let go, and the shaving sprang back into a tight curl right around his finger. David John thought this was such fun he did it again.

"I expect Jesus liked doing that, too," smiled his mother.

"What?" exclaimed David John, so surprised that he

nearly dropped his shaving. "What did you say, Mother?"

"Well, you enjoy being with Daddy when he's doing jobs, don't you? So when Jesus was your age, I expect he liked watching Joseph working in his carpenter's shop," answered Mother.

"Then did he help, too? Did he hold the wood steady while Joseph sawed it, and find the right nails for him, and did the sawdust smell as nice as ours does?" asked David John.

"Even nicer, if it was cedarwood," nodded Mother.

"Did Joseph have tools like Daddy?" asked Susan, coming in from the garden with the carrots for dinner.

"Oh, yes," said her mother, "and some of them were almost the same as Daddy's are today."

"Then go on, Mother—tell us!" demanded David John.

When Mother had found a knife and had begun to scrape the carrots, she said:

"Jesus was only a little boy when Joseph and Mary brought him home to Nazareth. There they settled down in Joseph's tiny flat-roofed house. It wasn't a bit like ours. In

fact, there was only one room in it. Except for sleeping mats, there was scarcely any furniture, and their donkey and the other animals lived there with them."

"Well, I would like *that!*" interrupted David John.

"The animals lived at one end, and the family at the other, where the floor was higher," went on Mother, "and though it wasn't much of a house, Joseph had made it as comfortable as he could for Mary and her little son. As for Jesus, he was happy all day long. He went to the market with his mother, holding her hand because it was so crowded and noisy, and together they got water from the village well in a great stone jar which Mary carried on her head. While Mary and the other women chatted beside the well, Jesus would play with the children who had come with their mothers, too.

"Back in the little house, he would watch his mother spin the soft sheep's wool, then dye it in bright colors, and weave it into striped cloth. Every day he watched her grind the corn, mix the flour into dough, then bake the small flat loaves that tasted so good. But at last he was old enough to go to school."

"School?" exclaimed Susan, looking very surprised.

"Oh, yes, Jesus went to school," said her mother, "but not to a school like yours. There were no girls at all, and he and the other boys had to sit on the floor of the synagogue. This was really the church, but it was used for a meeting place as well. There the priests taught them to read and write, and made them learn a lot of the holy Jewish laws by heart."

"And after school?" asked David John.

"Why, as soon as the priests let them out, the boys ran off to play," smiled Mother. "They dawdled home through the village, stopping to watch anything interesting on the way. Jesus was the sort of boy who noticed everything. He noticed the potter molding the wet clay into tall water jars and slender-necked bottles to keep the precious oil cool, dark, and sweet.

"He watched men building houses. He saw the slow oxen pulling the plow over the rough fields. Then he watched the sowers flinging the golden seed far and wide over the plowed earth, and at last, he saw men harvesting the ripe corn while he and his mother, and all the other village women, followed behind to pick up any stalks of corn the harvesters dropped. At home he watched his mother patching his worn clothes—for they were far too poor to have new clothes while old ones would do—and in the street outside he saw friendly happy children playing together, and sulky ones who wouldn't join in."

"Y-yes, but—" interrupted Susan, "how do you *know* all this?"

"You aren't making it up, are you, Mother?" asked David John anxiously.

"No," smiled Mother. "When he was grown up, Jesus talked about all these things, so he must have noticed them. A bright-eyed boy like Jesus didn't miss anything. When he went into the hills and the quiet country places, he noticed the foxes and discovered their secret holes, he watched the birds and saw their hidden nests, he gazed at the bright wild flowers and probably picked the best to take home to his mother.

"But best of all, he loved to see the shepherds leading their flocks. He may have helped, too, for he certainly knew a great deal about a shepherd's life, and loved the sheep—especially the little lost ones."

Suddenly Susan gave a jump.

"I know!" she shouted. "There's a story about a lost sheep—and it was Jesus who told it! So it *is* true!"

"That's right, Susan!" smiled Mother.

"I want to hear that story, too," said David John.

"Then I'll tell it to you one day," his mother promised, and went on. "So Jesus learned things in school, in the village, in the countryside, and in his own home, too. As he grew bigger and stronger, Joseph let him help more and more. He chopped and he sawed, he cut joints that fitted firm and true, he shaped crooks for the shepherds, and yokes for the necks of the patient oxen. If there were any bits of wood left over, I expect he made toys."

"Toy lambs and donkeys?" suggested David John.

"Yes, very likely," agreed Mother.

"The tails must have been hard to make," said David John.

"But didn't his mother teach him anything?" asked Susan.

"Oh, yes, a great deal," answered Mother. "She told him stories of heroes and kings, of prophets and priests, of battles and wars, of adventures and miracles. She taught him poetry, and sang him the old songs which she knew so well."

"Oh, Mother! You must be making it up!" frowned Susan.

"No," said her mother. "We know, because when

29

Mary was so happy and excited to hear that God was sending her his little son, she made up a song which is so beautiful that, after nearly two thousand years, we still sing it. And that song of praise to God is full of pieces she remembered from the poems and songs of her people. If she remembered them so well, I'm sure she taught them to Jesus, too."

"It was a nice way for him to grow up, wasn't it?" said Susan thoughtfully.

"Specially with the carpenter's shop, and all the animals," broke in David John.

"Yes," nodded Mother. "And there in the little house that smelled of sawdust and cedarwood, Jesus grew up wise, strong, and gentle, and everyone loved him."

"Specially the animals," added David John, as he ran to open the door for his cat, who was asking to come in.

"WHEN I grow up," said David John, "I'm going to be a bus driver."

"Whatever for?" asked Susan.

"Because I could drive all day, all over town," answered David John. Then he remembered something.

"Mother," he asked, "what did Jesus want to be when he grew up?"

"I expect he wanted to be the village carpenter," said Mother, "and so he was, for several years."

"Like Fred who mended our door?" interrupted David John, and Mother nodded.

"But at last," she went on, "it was time for him to begin his real job."

"What job?" demanded David John.

"Why, showing people what God is like, of course," answered Susan.

"Didn't they know, then?"

"They didn't know God as Jesus knew him," Mother explained. "They thought of God as a very stern, strict master, who expected them to obey all sorts of complicated rules and regulations, and who would be very angry if they forgot, and would punish them. But Jesus knew that God is our Father, who loves us and wants us to be good and happy."

"What did Jesus do?" asked David John.

"He decided that he must go about the country, telling the good news to as many people as he could," Mother continued. "So one day he said good-bye to his mother and his family and set off."

"That sounds like the beginning of an adventure," said David John, hugging his knees to listen better.

"And it was—a very great adventure," Mother

agreed. "But the people of Nazareth shook their heads in amazement. Why did such a clever young carpenter give up a steady job to go tramping over the countryside, teaching, helping, and healing complete strangers? His new life was certainly hard, and Jesus was often tired, dusty, and footsore. He seldom knew where he would be able to sleep, and the only food he had was given to him by people almost as poor as himself."

"And I expect he was lonesome sometimes, too," said David John.

"But before long," said Mother, "Jesus made friends who loved him so much that they went with him on his travels."

"Oh, good!" beamed David John, wriggling closer. "Go on, Mother, tell us."

"Well, one day Jesus was preaching on the shore of the great Sea of Galilee when the people began to crowd round him. In the shallow water nearby, two barelegged fishermen were washing their nets, while their boat rocked gently beside them. 'May I sit in your boat?' asked Jesus. The fishermen nodded, and followed him aboard. 'Push off a little way,' said Jesus, and when the boat was a short distance from the shore, Jesus turned to the crowd on the beach, and talked to them."

"That was a good idea," agreed David John, "but didn't the fishermen mind?"

"Peter, the owner, wasn't the sort of man to mind lending anyone a hand," said his mother. "When Jesus had finished talking he thanked the fishermen in a most wonderful way. 'Sail off into deep water,' he said, 'and let down your nets.' Peter sighed wearily. 'Master, we have fished all night long,' he said, 'and have caught *nothing!* But, since you say so, we'll try once more.'

"So, as soon as the water was deep enough, they let down their nets. In a moment they had caught so many fish that the nets began to break as they hauled them aboard.

Scarcely believing their eyes they waved and shouted to their partners in another boat, who came to help them.

"Then Peter was very frightened," Mother continued. "He fell on his knees before this strange passenger whom even the fishes obeyed. 'Lord, go away from me,' he whispered, 'for I am not good enough to be near you.' But Jesus shook his head and smiled. 'Don't be afraid,' he said, 'for I will make you a fisher of men.' And although Peter didn't quite understand how he was to catch men's hearts and souls, he knew without any doubt that he had found the master whom he would follow all his life. As soon as the fish were safely landed, Peter strode up the beach after his wonderful friend. A moment later, Peter's brother Andrew hurried after them."

"He didn't want to be left behind," nodded David John.

"Their partners, James and his brother John, had started to mend the broken nets. They looked up and saw Jesus walking away from them. Suddenly, they knew what they must do. Without a word they flung down their nets and followed him," said Mother.

"Just like that?" cried David John, and his mother nodded.

"So Jesus found four friends!" he exclaimed. "I think it was nice that they were brothers, don't you?"

"Yes, very nice," said Mother. "And the next day, two neighbors, Philip and Nathaniel, joined them."

David John was counting. "That made six!" he said.

"Before long, six more men joined the group," his mother continued, "and although many others followed

Jesus, these twelve were his dearest friends, and worked most closely with him."

"Like a team," Susan suggested, and her mother agreed.

"As these twelve watched Jesus healing, helping, and teaching, day after day, they began to understand what God was like, and to love and trust him," Mother went on. "But still they didn't know how to talk to God, or to ask his help. So they went to Jesus. 'Lord, teach us to pray,' they pleaded."

"But it's easy! I know how!" exclaimed David John. "I say, 'God bless Mother, and Daddy, and Susan, and—'"

"I say another prayer as well," Susan interrupted, "the one that Mother taught me. It begins, Our Father—"

"And that is the very prayer that Jesus taught his friends," smiled Mother.

"*What?* The one Susan says?" cried David John, looking very surprised. "Then go on, Susan, say it now!"

So Susan began, "Our Father, which art in Heaven, hallowed be Thy name. Thy kingdom come, Thy will be done, in earth as it is in heaven. Give us this day our daily bread, and forgive us our trespasses as we forgive them that trespass against us. And lead us not into temptation, but deliver us from evil; for Thine is the kingdom, the power and the glory for ever and ever. Amen."

"That's *hard!*" frowned David John.

"It only sounds hard because Susan is saying it in the old words," said Mother, "just as people have been doing for hundreds of years. But we will say it in our own words."

"Yes, I think we'd better," agreed David John. "Go on, Mother."

"Our Father, who lives in heaven," she began, "we pray that your name may be kept holy, that your kingdom of love may come, that all men may obey you, and that everyone in the world may do these things."

David John nodded. He understood it all so far.

"Give us our food, day by day," Mother continued, and David John was glad that Jesus hadn't forgotten about food.

"And forgive us when we do wrong," added Mother.

David John knew how important that was, because even he was naughty sometimes, and nothing was quite right until he had been forgiven.

"—forgive us, in the same way as we forgive people who have done wrong to us," said Mother.

At that, David John sat up very straight. So he would have to forgive Susan when he was cross with her, if he wanted God to forgive him! That would be hard, but he could see that it was fair.

"Do not let us give way to temptation, and save us from all harm," the prayer ended, "for the kingdom of love, its greatness and its glory, are yours for ever and ever."

"Amen," said David John, and was quiet for a moment. "Well, I understood all that," he added slowly, "but was it *really* the prayer that Jesus made up?"

"Yes, the Lord's Prayer is his very own prayer," answered Mother, "and though nearly two thousand years have passed since Jesus first said it, people have been saying it in every land and in every language ever since."

"All those people say it?" murmured David John. "And Susan says it?"

His mother nodded.

"And now, *I* say it too!" he cried, and ran to find his father and tell him all about it.

THE FOUR FRIENDS

"Ooh—ow—ooh!" shouted David John as he tried to get up from the floor, where he had been curled up with Tommy, the cat.

"Whatever is the matter?" exclaimed Susan.

"Ow! Ooh! My foot's gone to sleep! It's full of pins and needles!" squealed her brother.

"What a fuss!" laughed Susan. "Cheer up! You aren't para—para—what's that word, Mother?"

"Do you mean paralyzed?" asked her mother.

"Like the man with the four friends," said Susan.

"I don't know what you are talking about," grumbled David John, "and anyway, what about my leg?" Suddenly he wriggled it, and stamped his foot on the floor. "That's funny!" he grinned, "it's all right again now. Hooray!"

"I expect that's what the man said, too," smiled Mother.

"Yes," said Susan, "—*afterward!*"

At that, David John, who had been jumping up and down to make sure his leg would work, stopped.

"What man? What friends? And afterward, *what?*" he shouted.

"Why, it's a story about Jesus," Susan explained.

"Then why doesn't somebody tell it to *me?*" demanded David John. So Mother picked up the red sweater she was knitting, and began.

"Well, if ever a man needed friends, this man did. For his whole body was trembling and useless, and no amount of stamping and wriggling would make his legs and arms work. One day one of his friends came hurrying home from Capernaum. 'Listen!' he cried, 'there is a man in the town called Jesus, who is healing all sorts of sick people. Let's ask him to make our friend well!' The others shook their heads. 'How can a paralyzed man get to Capernaum?' they frowned. 'It's miles away.' 'But he's got four strong friends, hasn't he?' replied the other. 'Why shouldn't we carry him there?' "

"Well, that was a good idea," said David John, "but it sounds like a big job."

"So it would have been," agreed Mother, "if they hadn't remembered the thin mattress on which the man lay. With ropes at each corner, it made a good stretcher."

"Joggly, though," murmured David John.

"Yes, and by the time they reached Capernaum," his mother continued, "the poor man was very sick. But, through the narrow streets, people were hurrying forward. 'This way,' they called, 'this is the way to the house where Jesus is.' When the four faithful friends saw the crowd around the doorway, their hearts sank. Through the door they glimpsed a room packed with silent people, listening to a young man talking."

"I know," nodded David John, "it was Jesus."

"Suddenly the crowd stirred," Mother went on. " 'Make way for the scribes,' someone said, as some important-looking men pushed into the house. But when the friends tried to follow, the crowd would not let them pass.

The four men stared at each other in dismay. Jesus, only a few yards away, could cure their friend—that they knew. But how could they get their friend into the house? There was no other door, only the outside stairway leading up to the flat roof. Then one of them had an idea, and whispered to the others, who laughed and nodded at his extraordinary plan."

"What was it?" interrupted David John.

"Guess!" smiled Mother, but David John couldn't guess. Susan was pressing both hands over her mouth to keep from giving away the secret.

"Well, the roof was probably made with beams, across which rafters were laid, and was filled in with branches and twigs. Then the whole roof was covered with dirt, packed flat and hard," said Mother. "So, without a word, the men carried their friend up the stairway and laid him on the roof."

"Well, that didn't do the poor man any good," frowned David John.

"He probably thought the same," smiled Mother, "until he saw his friends start digging through the dirt on the roof, and he guessed how he was to get into the house."

"My goodness! You don't mean—" began David John, but Susan couldn't wait any longer.

"Yes," she interrupted, "they made a big hole in the roof, and let the man down!"

"Why didn't someone stop them?" asked David John.

"The people were all listening so hard to Jesus," answered Mother, "that they didn't notice anything until they saw the mattress lowered to the ground in front of him. 'How dare they! Disgraceful!' they cried, frowning angrily at the four friends, who were peering down through the roof."

"What about the poor man?" asked David John.

"When he found himself safe on the floor, he opened his eyes and looked up," said Mother.

"—and there was Jesus," whispered David John.

"Yes, Jesus was looking down at him and smiling at the strange way he had come in," Mother continued. "Jesus could see that he was very sick. He saw, too, that the man was anxious, miserable, and afraid that Jesus would guess all the bad things that he had done. Yet Jesus knew that any man who had such faithful friends must have some good in him.

"Jesus leaned down, and spoke softly. 'Son,' he said, and the man looked up, surprised at that homely word. 'Son,' said Jesus, 'the wrong things you have done are for-given.' The man gazed up at those wonderful eyes looking down at him. Then a slow smile lit up his face. Why, it was as though a great weight had been lifted from his heart!

"He felt so free, so clean, so happy," said Mother, "that he scarcely heard the gasp of horror that went up from the scribes. How *dare* this village carpenter pretend to for-give sins? Only God himself could do that! Then Jesus turned to them. 'I know what you are thinking,' he said sternly. 'But tell me—is it easier to say to this man, your sins are forgiven, or to tell him to get up and walk?' "

"W-well—" murmured David John doubtfully.

"The scribes shrugged their shoulders and laughed," his mother went on, "for it was easy to *say* things! But they didn't think this man would risk trying to cure a paralyzed

44

man with all these people watching! Then Jesus surprised them. 'But to show you that God has given me power to forgive—' he began, and turned back to the helpless man at his feet. The crowd was still. The four friends held their breath. Now the eyes of Jesus blazed with power, and the gentle voice rang out in commands that must be obeyed. 'Get up,' he said. Without a word, the man sprang to his feet. 'Pick up your bed!' said Jesus. Stooping swiftly, the man rolled up his mattress, and threw it onto his shoulder. 'And go back to your own home,' smiled Jesus. With one look of love and gratitude, the man turned and marched away, as straight as a soldier. The silent crowds drew back to let him pass, scarcely able to believe their own eyes. 'We have never seen such a wonderful miracle,' they whispered, as they went quietly away."

"I guess they hadn't," said David John. "But what about the four friends?"

"I expect they stayed to mend the roof," answered Mother.

David John nodded, then suddenly looked up. "If any of the wooden rafters were broken, do you think Jesus borrowed some tools and mended them?"

"I wouldn't be a bit surprised," smiled Mother.

"Neither would I!" said David John.

A LITTLE GIRL WAKES UP

"Isn't breakfast ready *yet?*" asked David John. "I'm hungry!"

"Why, you've just waked up!" laughed Susan.

"Well, I always wake up hungry. All boys do. Everyone knows that!"

"Jesus did, anyway—and I expect that little girl was very hungry when *she* woke up," said Susan, as Mother called them from the kitchen door.

"Hooray! Breakfast—and sweet rolls, too!" shouted David John, clambering up into his chair. And it wasn't until he was halfway through his scrambled egg that he remembered.

"Susan, *what* little girl woke up hungry?" he demanded.

"You tell, Mother," said Susan, busy with her toast. So, as it was Saturday, and not a school morning, Mother poured herself another cup of coffee and began.

"This little girl was twelve years old," she began.

"Like Betsy," nodded Susan.

"Not very big, though," murmured David John.

"No," agreed his mother, "in fact, she looked very little as she lay in bed, so white and still. She was sick. Every doctor in Capernaum had tried to make her better, for Jairus, her father, was a great man, and one of the most important people in the church, and she was his only child."

"No brothers, then?" sighed David John, "—not even a sister!"

"The little girl grew weaker and weaker," Mother continued, "and her father began to give up hope. 'If only that new preacher were here!' sobbed her mother. 'They tell me that he has healed many sick people—why, he even cured a paralyzed man!' "

"I know," said David John, "it was the man with four friends! Go on, Mother."

"Jairus shook his head," said Mother. " 'It's no good! He isn't here,' he sighed. 'He's gone away, across the Sea

of Galilee, and no one knows when he'll come back to Capernaum.' 'Master,' cried one of his servants, 'if you mean Jesus, why, he's on his way home now! When I went down to buy fresh fish, I saw Peter's boat come sailing toward the beach with a fine fresh wind.' Then Jairus' eyes lit up with a great hope, and without another word he turned and ran to the shore. And there stood Jesus."

"Oh, *good!*" whispered David John, as his mother continued.

"Jesus looked up as he heard the sharp crunch of feet running down the beach. 'Why, it's Jairus!' gasped a man in the crowd which had gathered round Jesus. 'How worried he looks!' 'Whatever can be the matter?' asked his neighbor. And they soon heard, for as Jairus fell on his knees before Jesus, he panted, 'My little girl is dying. Come, I beg you! Only touch her, and she will live!' At once Jesus turned and went with Jairus."

"Oh, I hope they hurried up!" frowned David John anxiously.

"Yes, they did," nodded Mother. "Peter, James, and John, who were hauling the boat up onto the beach, had to run to catch them. The excited crowd followed, eager to see what Jesus would do. But they hadn't gone very far when one of Jairus' servants came toward them. Jairus looked at his face, and he knew. 'Your daughter is dead,' said the man. 'Don't bother Jesus any more.'"

"They were too late!" sighed David John.

"That was what the servant thought," his mother agreed, "and so did Jairus. But Jesus turned and looked straight into his eyes. 'Fear not,' he said, 'only trust in God!' But the poor father's mind was in a whirl as he followed Jesus, striding ahead, so calm and sure. 'Don't be afraid—just trust!' said Jesus. Yet how could anyone, even Jesus, cure a child who was already dead? Then Peter moved up quietly closer. 'Trust him, Jairus; only trust him!' he whispered. 'Jesus cured my own wife's mother— and I was there!' 'Go on trusting,' added James, 'for even

50

the fishes obey him—we have seen them with our own eyes.' 'Trust him, Jairus, trust him with all your heart,' urged John, 'for the very lepers are made clean at his touch—we stood beside him as he healed them.' At that, Jairus' head lifted, and his eyes glowed with hope. Yet when he reached the house, and heard the loud sobbing and wailing of all those who had come to mourn his little daughter, his heart sank.

"But now Jesus took command," Mother continued. "He walked straight into the room where the little girl lay, and stood looking down at her. 'She isn't dead,' he said quietly, 'she's only asleep.' At that, a great laugh went up from the crowded room. 'Listen to that! Did you ever hear such nonsense!' jeered the people. 'Just look at her! Anyone can see she's dead.'

"Jesus did not argue. Instead, he sent all the people out of the child's room."

"Oh, not her mother and father!" protested David John.

"Of course, Jesus let *them* stay, and his three friends as well," his mother assured him. "Then he waited until the room was very quiet, and in the stillness, he leaned over the child, and took her hand in his. 'Up you come, little girl,' he said gently. And as her mother held her breath, the child slowly opened her eyes, and looked up."

"And there was Jesus," whispered David John.

"—and there was Jesus smiling down at her," nodded Mother. "Still clinging to that strong hand, she sat up, looked around, and saw her mother and father. Then she stood up, straight and steady, as her mother's arms

51

closed round her. She was a happy little girl again."

"Oh, good, good, *good!*" beamed David John, hitting his knee three times because he was so pleased. "Then what, Mother?"

"Well, then," smiled Mother, "while her mother was kissing her, and her father was hugging her, and Peter, James, and John were almost dancing with joy, what *do* you think Jesus said?"

"Goodness! I don't know," exclaimed David John.

"He said, 'Give her something to eat,' " cried Mother.

But David John wasn't a bit surprised.

"Of course," he said. "Jesus knew she'd be hungry when she woke up, because he was *sensible*. I wonder what her mother gave her?"

"Some bread and honey, and a warm drink, I expect," answered his mother.

"And that reminds me," exclaimed David John, looking at his empty plate, "I'd like some more rolls, because *I'm* hungry, too!"

52

THE LITTLE FISHES

"YES, BUT—" frowned David John as he looked at Susan's book about Jesus, "but aren't there any stories with *boys* in them?"

Susan thought for a moment, then whispered to Mother.

"Why, of course," exclaimed Mother, "the boy with the fishes!"

"Then go on, Mother, tell me about that boy," pleaded David John.

"Well, come and help me polish the spoons," suggested his mother, who was cleaning the silver. So, as David John laughed at his own face, upside down in the first shiny spoon, she began.

"There was a warm nutty smell coming from the little house by the Sea of Galilee," she said, "and the boy standing at the doorway sniffed, poked his head inside, and nodded. Yes, his mother was baking flat barley loaves, crisp and round. But as he heard the sound of hurrying footsteps, he turned back to the street.

"There, coming round the corner, he saw a crowd of people. Who were they, he wondered, and why were they looking so puzzled and disappointed? 'Have you seen him?' asked one. 'He isn't in Capernaum—is he here?' 'Who?' demanded the boy. 'Why, Jesus, of course,' they answered. Then the boy's sharp eyes narrowed as he gazed across the great lake. Suddenly he pointed. 'See that boat with the patched sail, heading for the eastern shore? That's Peter's boat, and I can see some men on board—about a dozen of them.' 'So that's where Jesus has gone!' sighed the crowd, and turned away. But the boy had a better idea. 'Mother, Mother!' he called, 'may I go round the head of the lake to meet Jesus? His boat is heading for the Bethsaida shore, and it's only nine miles!' "

"But that's an awful long way!" broke in Susan.

"His mother thought the same," said Mother. " 'It's much too far for a boy,' she answered. 'But Mother,' pleaded the boy, 'I can take some food, and have a picnic there.' 'W-well, be back before dark, mind!' she said. 'And now I suppose you'll want some of my fresh barley loaves—so here you are, three hot ones!' 'Oh, good!' beamed the boy, 'but I shall get very hungry, Mother. May I take four—no, *five* loaves? And what about one of those little pickled fish—or, better still, *two,* Mother?' 'Why, you eat more than your father!' chuckled his mother, as she gave him the fishes as well. Even the poorest people, who, like themselves, had to make do with barley bread, always had some little pickled fishes for a relish."

"I know—like sardines for a snack," interrupted David John.

"So the boy wrapped his picnic lunch in a cloth," nodded Mother, "and tucked it into the wide sash he wore round his tunic—for that was where he stuffed all the things he wanted to carry."

"What? No pockets for a piece of string, or a curly shell, or—or anything else that you might need?" exclaimed David John.

"No pockets at all, but the sash did as well," said his mother, "and I suspect he carried just as many funny things there as you do in your pockets."

David John grinned. "Well, what about all those other people?" he asked.

"The boy wasn't the only one to think of going round the head of the lake," Mother continued, "and as there wasn't much wind, the walkers soon caught up with the boat. They waded through the shallow River Jordan, where it flowed into the lake—and the boy laughed for fun as he splashed through—and they were there on the lonely eastern shore when the boat landed. There were no houses in sight. It was springtime, so the grass was green. It would have been quiet there for Jesus, if the crowd had left him in peace. But though he sighed as he saw them clustering round him, he felt so sorry for them that he couldn't send them away. So he helped them, and talked to them, and the small boy, wriggling his way to the front, watched and listened until the sun started to sink over the lake.

"One of the disciples, Jesus' special friends, began to look anxious. 'Master,' he interrupted, 'send all these people away now, so they can find some place where they can get food, for it's getting late, and this is a very deserted spot.' 'If they are hungry, feed them,' answered Jesus calmly. At that, Philip gasped in amazement. 'But a mouthful each for such a crowd would cost several hundred dollars,' he frowned, 'and that's a month's wages for any working man!' *Oh, dear,* thought the boy, *Philip wasn't being much help. But, after all, no one could help, unless*—and then he had an idea! *He* had some food, hadn't he? If he gave it to Jesus, why, there was no knowing what Jesus could do, with even a small boy's picnic!"

"That *was* a good idea," said David John, "and then what?"

"But the boy felt much too shy to go marching up to Jesus alone. Philip was talking, Peter was far too important, and none of the men near Jesus looked as though they'd have much time for boys. Then he noticed Andrew, Peter's brother, in the background as usual, as though he too, might be rather shy. Yes, *he* might listen, even to a boy. So, with-

56

out a word to anybody, the boy edged up to Andrew and pulled at his sleeve. 'Please—please,' he said, 'if Jesus wants to feed all these people, he can have *my* picnic.' Andrew glanced at the huge crowd, then looked down at the five barley loaves and two small fishes. But he didn't laugh. Putting a friendly hand on the boy's shoulder, he led him straight to Jesus. 'There is a boy here who has five barley loaves and two small fishes,' he began. Then he saw the expression on Philip's face, and looked down at the loaves and fishes. They looked very, very small. 'But what are *they,* among so many?' he added, hoping that Jesus wouldn't laugh. And Jesus didn't. 'Make the people sit down!' he said. And soon, on the fresh grass, in groups of fifties and hundreds, the people settled down, looking, in their bright clothes, like great flower beds set in a green lawn."

"But why did they have to sit down?" asked David John.

"So they wouldn't get squashed up and muddled, and start pushing each other about," Susan explained.

"Oh!" murmured her brother. "Jesus was very sensible, wasn't he, Mother?"

His mother nodded and went on. "Then Jesus looked down at the boy and smiled. Without a word, the boy put everything he had into the hands of Jesus."

"All five loaves? *And* his two fishes?"exclaimed David John. "That boy was a good giver! Then what, Mother?"

"First, Jesus said grace, just as the boy's father did," Mother went on, "and then, when he had given thanks to God, something so wonderful happened that the boy could not believe his eyes. For as the strong, loving hands of Jesus

broke the bread and gave it, there was sufficient for all the five thousand hungry people, and even the two small fishes were enough to go round. The boy watched, round-eyed and silent, as the food was handed to the crowd, until at last everyone had eaten all he could."

David John let out his breath in a long sigh of wonder. Then he remembered something.

"That boy!" he said. "Did he get anything?"

"Indeed he did!" said Mother. "He ate as much as any hungry boy can eat at a picnic—and that's a lot!"

"And after that, he felt better," nodded David John.

"Much better," his mother agreed. "But the disciples were already collecting the leftovers—and there were twelve baskets full. Now the sun was low in the sky, and it was a long way home. When the boy set off, Jesus looked up, and lifted his hand in farewell. As the boy trotted along the shore, the waterbirds were settling sleepily in the reedbeds, and a fish rose, making wide circles in the lake which gleamed gold and crimson in the sunset. The moon was rising when he arrived home, rather dirty, and very tired. But when he told his mother how Jesus had fed the five thousand people, he was the proudest boy in the land."

"And what's more," added David John, "that boy helped, too."

"He was a sort of partner, wasn't he?" said Susan, "and that's what Jesus wants us to be, isn't it, Mother?"

"Even boys?" asked David John.

"Even the smallest boy," replied his mother.

"That's good," murmured David John, and picked up another spoon.

THE GOOD FRIEND

"MOTHER, MOTHER, the chain came off my bicycle, and Henry stopped and put it on for me, though he was in a hurry, so can he wash his hands, and here he is!" shouted David John, all in one breath, as he burst into the kitchen one Saturday morning.

"Well, you are a Good Samaritan, and on your busy day, too," smiled Mother as she turned on the hot water for Henry, who had brought the groceries from Mr. Martin's store.

"That was a funny name you called Henry, Sam— Sam something!" grinned David John.

"Ho, ho! You mean a Good Samaritan!" laughed Henry.

"Is it a nice thing to be called, then?" asked David John.

"Yes, very, and here's a cup of chocolate for him," said Mother.

"Ah! I always liked that story," nodded Henry.

"If it's a story, tell it to me, Mother!" cried David John.

"Help me to unpack the groceries, then," said his mother. So, as soon as David John had seen Henry off at the gate, she began.

"This is one of the stories that Jesus told," she said.

"Why, did he tell stories, too?" interrupted David John.

"Lots of stories, about all sorts of things!" exclaimed Susan. "Why, whenever he had anything hard to explain, he told a story about it to make it easier to understand. Oh, and those special stories were called parables, weren't they, Mother?"

"Right," nodded her mother, "and this was one of them."

"Jesus told this parable because he wanted people to be friends with everyone," Susan added.

"Shush, Susan," frowned David John, "and let Mother go on with the story."

"Well, as Susan says, Jesus knew that all men are brothers, whatever color they are, whatever country they come from, and whether they are on our side or not," said Mother.

"That's hard to understand," said David John.

"That's what the people listening to Jesus thought," agreed his mother. "They knew they should be kind to their families and their friends, and even to their neighbors who lived in the same village or the same street. But as to strangers and foreigners, why, they hated them, and always

had. So Jesus told them this story about a man who was walking from Jerusalem down to Jericho.

"It was only about twenty miles, but the road twisted and turned through the hills from the city high in the mountains, down and down to the hot, damp town of Jericho, where palm trees grew. The traveler saw nothing but the rocky hillside, but there were robbers hiding there who saw him, walking alone. Swiftly they swooped down on the traveler, snatched all he had, tore off his clothes, then fled to their caves among the rocks, leaving him half dead."

"I hope someone came to help him," sighed David John.

"Soon, a man from the Temple came along the road," said his mother.

"Good!" interrupted David John.

"—but he did not even stop. He passed by on the other side of the road, pretending not to see," said Mother.

"Oh, *no!*" cried David John, wide-eyed with surprise.

"Before long, another man, who had probably been singing in the Temple services, came along," his mother said.

"Then I expect he was a good man," said David John.

"The traveler thought so too, and gave a sigh of relief as the man crossed the road, and stood looking down at his wounds," said Mother. "But after a moment, the man turned away, and passed by on the other side."

"Oh, how *could* he?" cried David John.

"And as his footsteps died away in the distance," Mother went on, "the wounded traveler almost gave up hope. When he heard the clip-clop of a donkey's hooves coming along the road, he scarcely lifted his head. And as he saw that the donkey's rider was a foreigner from Samaria, he closed his eyes with a groan, for the Samaritans and the Jews were bitter enemies. No Samaritan would help a Jew, that was certain, he thought, waiting for the sound of trotting to fade away again.

"But suddenly the noise stopped. The donkey had halted. There was the slap-slap of sandals on the road, very near, then the touch of a cool hand on his head. At last the traveler looked up, and there knelt the Samaritan, his eyes full of pity and kindness."

"Well, that foreigner was a good man, much better than those others," said David John, "but what did he do?"

"He just did the best he could," answered Mother. "He had no ointment, only some oil and wine. But wine would help to clean the wounds, and oil would soothe and heal them. He had no bandages, so he tore strips from his own clothes, and bound up the traveler's wounds as best he could. Then he fetched his patient donkey, who was searching for tufts of grass along the roadside, and lifted the wounded man onto his back. Now, very gently, he led the donkey along the road to Jericho."

"I hope that donkey didn't joggle the poor man," said David John.

"The good donkey picked his way carefully over the stony road," nodded his mother, "until at last he saw the inn ahead. The donkey halted in the courtyard while his master and the innkeeper carried the wounded man into the house, where they made him as comfortable as they could."

"And what about the donkey?" asked David John.

"He enjoyed his supper, and then had a nice long rest," answered Mother. "But his master didn't get much sleep that night, for he had the wounded man to look after. Next morning, the donkey felt fresh and lively, but the Samaritan shook his head as he saw that the traveler was far too ill to go on to Jericho. So he gave the innkeeper some money. 'Take care of him,' he said, 'and if you have to spend more than this, I will settle up with you next time I come this way.' "

"Goodness! That might have cost him a lot of money," exclaimed David John.

"It probably did," his mother agreed.

"And he was a foreigner," added Susan, "not a relative or even a friend."

"He *was* a friend—the best friend in the world!" protested David John.

"He certainly was," nodded Mother.

"So that's why you called Henry a Good Samaritan," murmured David John. And then he thought of something else. "Yes, but—" he added, "he couldn't have taken that poor man to the inn without the donkey, so the donkey was a friend too, wasn't he, Mother?"

"That's right," smiled Mother, and ruffled his hair.

"WHAT SHALL I buy?" David John asked his mother, as he stared at the candy in Mr. Martin's store. He had found a dime in his pocket and was anxious to spend it.

"Well, make up your mind," said Mother, "because I'm ready to go."

David chose a crunchy chocolate bar wrapped in gold paper.

"We may meet Susan, who will be coming back from her piano lesson, so save some candy for her," Mother reminded him.

"Oh, I will," said David John. Surely enough as they got to the corner of their street, there was Susan coming home also. She was pleased with the candy and didn't say a word about its being a rather small piece David John had left for her. Nor did David John for he had seen a baby lamb, munching grass in the yard of a nearby house.

"See the lamb!" he shouted. And just then he

remembered something else. "Mother, you haven't told me that story. And you promised."

"What story?" asked Susan.

"The one about the lost lamb," said David John. "Was the lost lamb like the one in the yard?"

"Well, yes," said Mother, "except that those sheep had quite different tails, very short and fat."

"They must have looked funny!" said David John. "Did the shepherds have dogs to help them watch the sheep?"

"Oh, no," answered his mother. "The shepherds never drove their sheep. They always led them."

"Led them? But how?" exclaimed David John in great surprise.

"Well, if you wanted your cat to come," asked Mother, "what would you do?"

"That's easy!" laughed David John. "I'd just call him."

"And he knows your voice, so he would come," nodded his mother. "That's just what the sheep did when their shepherd called them, for they too, knew his voice. Day and night he watched over them. Even when they were in the sheepfold, he lay all night across the doorway, so that no enemy should attack them.

"Then, as the sun rose, he would call his sheep, and, however many other sheep were in the fold, his sheep, and only his, would trot after him as he led them to some quiet pasture where they could safely graze. And grass wasn't always easy to find in that country. With his long shepherd's crook and his strong staff to protect them from wild animals, he would take them safely over mountains, along dangerous paths, through streams and rivers, never hurrying the mother sheep and their babies, until at last he brought them to where the grass was sweet."

"I like hearing about those sheep," said David John, "but what about my story, Mother?"

"Well, this is another of the stories that Jesus told," said his mother.

"One of those special stories?" asked the boy.

"Yes, it was a parable," nodded Mother. "One day, some important men were criticizing Jesus for making friends with people who, they felt sure, were not good enough for him to know. Jesus wondered how he could explain that God loves every one of us, and that every single one of us matters just as much to him. 'Ah, sheep!' thought Jesus.

'They all know about sheep, they've all seen shepherds with their flocks, so I will tell them a story about a sheep.' And so he did."

"Then go on, Mother—please, Mother!" pleaded David John.

" 'Once upon a time,' said Jesus, 'there was a shepherd who had a hundred sheep. The spring was over, and the grass was no longer green and fresh; in fact, it was hard to find any grass at all for his sheep to eat. So he decided to lead them to a faraway place he knew of, beyond the hills. It was wild and rocky country, and in many places the track was narrow and dangerous.

" 'He often had to stop to call the stragglers, and wait for them to catch up, but at last he brought his sheep to the grassy valley where they could feed in peace. The shepherd

gave a sigh of relief as he stood watching them. Suddenly he frowned. *Were* there a hundred sheep? Quickly he counted them—then counted again, to make sure. There were only ninety-nine feeding there! And he knew the very one which was missing—that frisky lamb who was now too big to stay with his mother. The shepherd was tired, and hungry, too. The mountains were dangerous, but he didn't hesitate. He left the ninety-nine sheep—they wouldn't stray while they had grass to eat!—and set off up the steep path to find the sheep that was lost.' "

"He was a *good* shepherd, wasn't he, Mother?" said David John.

" 'That good shepherd climbed the mountains,' " Mother went on, " 'he scrambled up the rocky slopes, for hour after hour he called and he searched, but still he could not find the lamb.' "

"What about the lamb?" asked David John.

" 'It was fun, thought the lamb, to run off by himself,' " Mother continued, " 'and he was feeling very clever, until suddenly he noticed that his shepherd had gone, and there wasn't another sheep in sight. Then the lamb thought he'd better catch up again. But which way had the flock gone? He didn't know. He ran one way, and then the other. 'Baa-aa!' he cried, 'where are you all?' No sheep bleated in answer, so he clambered up, higher and higher, but still he couldn't see a single sheep anywhere. So he leaped on up to a high, narrow ledge of rock—and there he was! He couldn't go on, and he couldn't turn back. He couldn't scramble up, and he couldn't slide down. 'Maa-aa! Maa-aa-aa!' he whimpered, but no one heard him.

70

" 'He began to feel very hungry, and very, very frightened. Yet however loudly he bleated, no one answered. The sun was sinking, and it would soon be dark. Just as he was giving up hope, he heard a voice calling, a voice that he knew. 'Baa-aa! Here I am, shepherd! Baa-aa-aa!' shouted the lamb at the top of his voice, and he didn't stop bleating until, at last, he saw his own shepherd climbing up toward him.' "

"Oh, how glad that lamb must have felt!" exclaimed David John.

" 'The shepherd was glad, too,' " said Mother, " 'so glad that he didn't think of the risk as he began the dangerous climb to rescue his lost lamb. The lamb was heavy, and not at all clean, yet the shepherd slung him across his shoulders like a shawl, grasped the four feet in his hands, and, somehow, managed to scramble down to the path. Footsore and hungry, he trudged on and on, and didn't stop until at last the lamb was back with the flock once more, safe and well.' "

"Oh, good!" said David John. "I expect the other sheep were glad to see him back again. But that bad lamb didn't really deserve to be found, did he, Mother?"

"No, not really," his mother agreed, "yet the shepherd was so happy to have found him again, that he called all his friends and neighbors to tell them the good news."

"All for one lamb?" murmured David John.

"That's what the people listening to Jesus' story thought," nodded Mother. "Now they understood that God, our Father, loves every single one of us, however small or bad we are, and when even one of his children comes home to God, why, he is full of joy."

71

THE SON WHO WAS SORRY

"Pooh! I wouldn't like to eat that stuff!" giggled David John as he and Susan watched Bob, the farmer's son, feeding the pigs. It was fun to see all the little pink ones, squealing at the top of their voices, wriggling and pushing to get at the food in the trough, although it certainly didn't smell very nice.

"How fast they're gobbling it up!" laughed Susan. "Why, even if I were as hungry as the Prodigal Son, I wouldn't want to eat *that!*"

"What son?" asked David John, "and why did he want to eat the pigs' food?"

"Well, to show the sort of father God is, Jesus told this story about a son who was sorry," said Susan. "But here comes Mother—ask her about it."

"Why can't *you* tell me this story?" demanded David John.

"If I start, Mother, will you tell us the rest?" asked

Susan, and began: "Once upon a time there was a man who had two sons who worked on the farm with the other farm laborers."

"Like Bob?" put in her brother.

"Yes, just like Bob," nodded Susan. "Their father was very rich, and they knew that when he died everything would be divided between them. But they had to work very hard in the fields, and the younger son didn't like it at all. 'If only I had that money *now*,' he thought, 'what a good time I could have!' So he went to his father and said, 'Father, give me my share.' "

"I don't suppose his father liked that very much," frowned David John.

"I don't suppose he did," his mother agreed, "but he gave the younger son his share, and in a very few days, as soon as he had got all the money together, the lad set off on his travels."

"That sounds exciting," said David John.

"And so it was," Mother replied. "Off he went, striding jauntily along the road, never once looking back to where his father stood, all alone, watching his son go away."

"And he didn't even wave!" sighed David John.

"On went the young man," Mother continued, "until he came to a foreign country, far away. 'Ho, ho! This is the place for a fine lad like me,' he laughed. 'Now I shall buy some splendid clothes, and have as many rich feasts as I like!' And so he did. He soon found plenty of people to eat his food and tell him how wonderful he was. '*This* is better than working on the farm!' he thought. 'This is the life for me!' And he was having such an exciting time that he didn't notice how fast his money was going until, one day, he found there was none left."

"Not any?" exclaimed David John.

"Not a penny!" answered his mother. " 'Ah well, all my fine friends will help me,' he said. But they didn't— not one of them. Worse still, there was a famine in that

land, and no one had anything at all to spare for the young foreigner. 'Hum! I shall have to get a job!' he frowned, but no one would give him work. Only one man offered him a job—and that was to look after his pigs. 'What? *Me*, a swine-herd?' he cried. 'Why, I will have nothing to do with pigs,' he said."

"So what did that young man do?" asked the boy.

"There was only one thing he *could* do," said his mother. "He took the job. Day after lonely day he guarded the pigs as they rooted for food in the bare fields, until he grew thin and weak, and his fine clothes were in rags. He was so hungry that he would have been glad to make a meal of the bean pods, which was all the food the farmer could spare for the pigs. But no one gave him any."

"Well, what did he do, Mother?" asked David John.

"He said to himself," Mother continued, " 'How many of my father's hired men are there who have food enough—and to spare! Yet here am I, starving! I will go to my father.' "

76

"That's good," nodded David John, "but what *was* he going to say to his father?"

"He was going to own up, and say he was sorry," said Mother. "He said to himself, 'I will say, "Father, I have done wrong, both to God and to you, and I'm not worth calling a son any more; but just let me work for you, as though I were a servant."''"

"Now tell about his father, Mother," said Susan.

"His father often watched the empty road," went on Mother, "looking for the gay, handsome lad who had gone that way long ago. But today, there was no one in sight, except a ragged, half-starved creature, some beggar, perhaps, who was limping slowly toward him. Then the father looked again—and although the traveler was still a long way off, he knew. It was his son! Without a moment's hesitation, the father ran to meet him, flung his arms round his son's neck and kissed him."

"Oh, good!" beamed David John. "But I expect that made the son feel very bad. Whatever did he say?"

"At first he couldn't manage to get out the words he had been repeating to himself all the way home," said Mother, "but at last he stammered, 'Father, I—I have done wrong, both to God and to you, and—and I'm not worth calling a son any more—' But his father didn't let him finish. 'Bring the best robe I've got,' he shouted to his servants, 'and put it on him! Put a ring on his finger, and shoes on his poor tired feet!' and as they ran to obey, he called, 'Bring the fat calf, kill it, and let us feast and be merry! For this, my son, was lost, and is found!' In a moment, the house became full of bustle and excitement as everyone hurried about making preparations for the feast."

"Now that the son had said he was sorry, I expect he felt better," murmured David John, who knew all about being naughty, and how hard it is to own up, and how good it feels to be forgiven. "But what about that big brother of his?"

"All day long the big brother had been working in the fields," Mother went on, "and as the sun sank, he plodded wearily home. But before he reached the house, he heard music and dancing, and the sound of happy voices. 'What is the meaning of this?' he called to a servant hurrying by. 'Why, your brother has come home,' answered the man, 'and your father has had us kill the fat calf for a feast,

because he has got his son safe home again.' Then the big brother was angry, and turned away, refusing to go in."

"I know why he was angry," interrupted David John, "it was because he thought it wasn't fair."

"When the servant told his master," Mother said, "he left the feast, and went alone to his son, to beg him to come in and welcome his young brother home, but he wouldn't. 'I have worked for you for many years,' he scowled, 'and never disobeyed you. Yet you never gave *me* anything— not even a lamb!—so that I could have a party for *my* friends! But when this other son of yours, who has thrown away all your money, turns up again, you give *him* the very calf we've been fattening for a special occasion!' "

"No wonder he felt it wasn't fair," murmured the boy.

"His father let his son have his say," said Mother, "then put his arm round his shoulders. 'Son,' he said quietly, 'you are always with me, and all that I have will be yours one day.' But his son didn't answer. 'It was right that we should be glad,' insisted his father, 'for this is your *brother* who was lost, and is found!' "

"He must have forgotten it was his little brother," nodded David John.

"When he remembered, I expect he felt much better," Mother added, "and ran straight to his brother and hugged him."

"Then he probably said, 'And I hope you've left some of the feast for *me,* because I'm hungry!' " laughed Susan.

"I'm hungry, too! What's for dinner today, Mother?" asked David John.

80

THE YOUNG DONKEY

"MOTHER, MOTHER! Come and look!" shouted David John, racing along the lane. "Duchess is in the meadow with her little colt!"

"I'm coming," called his mother as the two children scrambled onto the gate to see better. There was the mare with her colt, standing very close beside her.

"Ooh, isn't he lovely!" crooned Susan.

"What long legs he has!" exclaimed David John. "I expect he can gallop like anything!" And then he thought of something. "Mother! He's exactly the right size for me! Let me have a ride!"

"I don't think you'd stay on very long! That little colt would soon throw you off!"

"But why?" demanded David John.

"Well, boys have to learn to ride," said Mother, "and colts have to learn to be ridden."

"I hadn't thought of that," said the boy.

"Then it must have been rather frightening for that little donkey Jesus rode," remarked Susan slowly.

"He wouldn't have been frightened—not with Jesus," answered David John, "but you haven't told me about that donkey, Mother. What happened?"

"This is what happened," said his mother. "Jesus had been trying to explain that he had come to win men's hearts, not to conquer their enemies. But, for many, many years, the Jews had been hoping for some great king to come and drive out their conquerors, and make them great and free once more.

"Over and over again, Jesus had told them that his kingdom was a kingdom of love, not of force, yet still they did not understand. So he decided to show them. The great feast of the Passover was very near, and thousands of pilgrims were traveling to Jerusalem. Jesus and his disciples would be there, too. Now, everybody knew that when a great king rode forth to war, he rode a proud horse, but when a king came in peace, he rode a gentle donkey. So Jesus would ride up to Jerusalem on a donkey—and he knew the very one. Near Bethany, where Jesus often stayed with his friends, he had noticed a young donkey, standing close to its mother."

"Like Duchess and her baby?" interrupted David John.

"This one had never been ridden, either," nodded his mother. "I expect Jesus had asked the owner if he might borrow the little donkey one day, and probably he had patted and stroked him, too. And now the time had come. But Jesus was not hurrying to Jerusalem for a happy feast. He was going forward into certain danger. He knew that there were people who hated and feared him, and would do anything to get rid of him. Yet he set his face fearlessly toward Jerusalem, and went straight on. When he came to Bethany, not far from the city, he beckoned two of his disciples. 'Go into the village over there,' he said, 'and you'll soon see a young donkey tethered. Untie him, and bring him to me. If anyone asks you what you are doing, say, 'The Lord needs him.' ''

"So what did the two disciples do?" asked David John.

"They did just what Jesus told them," answered his mother, "and, sure enough, just inside the village, there was the colt. 'What are you doing, loosing that colt?' demanded the bystanders, as the disciples untied him. 'The Lord needs him,' they answered, and led the young donkey to Jesus."

"I expect that little colt wondered what was going to happen," said David John.

"At first, he did feel scared, and wanted to run home to his mother," Mother went on, "but as soon as Jesus spoke to him, and stroked his ears, the donkey knew that everything would be all right. So he didn't kick or bite when the disciples flung their cloaks across him, and Jesus sat on his back. He felt very strange, but with that quiet voice in his ears, and those strong, gentle hands holding the reins, he stepped out, steady and proud, on the road to Jerusalem."

"He was a *good* little donkey," beamed David John.

"And though it was a long pull up to the city," his mother continued, "the donkey didn't stumble or falter, even when the crowds began to gather round them. 'Hosanna!' they shouted, 'blessed is he who comes in the name of the Lord!' And they spread their bright cloaks on the roadway, tore green branches from the trees and laid them on the ground, and shouted for joy to welcome Jesus."

"Wasn't the donkey frightened?" asked David John.

"Without Jesus, the noise and excitement would have terrified him," his mother agreed, "but the donkey held his head high, proud to carry this wonderful rider. But there was one man close to Jesus who wasn't cheering, one man who frowned as he walked in silence, and scowled at the donkey beside him. That was Judas, the disciple who had never understood."

"What do you mean, Mother?" asked Susan, looking puzzled.

"Judas had believed that Jesus was the great conqueror," her mother explained, "come to drive the Roman

invaders away, and then reign in power and glory over Israel. But now, all his hopes were beginning to fade. The fame of Jesus had spread through the country like a flame. Wherever he went, crowds followed him. And today, the shouting, cheering multitude showed how much the people loved him. Why hadn't he marched on Jerusalem, at the head of an army, and proclaimed himself king? Why hadn't he ridden in on some great black charger, instead of a shy young donkey? Was *that* the way for a king to behave, Judas asked himself."

"I suppose he felt as though Jesus had let him down," said Susan thoughtfully.

"Yet Jesus had explained his kingdom, over and over again," answered Mother. "But Judas would not understand. If Jesus was the Son of God, then he must smash the enemies of his people, thought Judas. If Jesus would not do that, then he was not the leader for whom the nation had waited so long. So, however joyfully the crowd shouted, one man's heart was filled with bitterness as the branches of palm were waved to welcome Jesus."

"Then that's why the Sunday before Easter is called Palm Sunday!" exclaimed Susan.

"Right," smiled her mother.

"Now go on about the donkey," urged David John.

"The donkey was beginning to feel tired, for it had been a long climb," said Mother, "when at last they came in through the great gateway. There, in the narrow city streets, the people crowded so close that the donkey was glad when one of the disciples took his bridle and led him through the shouting, jostling throng.

"Now people leaned from their windows, and peered from their doorways. 'Who is this?' they cried. 'This is Jesus, Jesus of Nazareth!' answered the crowd. 'Jesus! Why, he healed my brother! It was he who cured my neighbor! I know a blind man who was given his sight by this Jesus! And I was there in Capernaum when he brought the little girl back to life! My son saw a paralyzed man stand up and march away when Jesus commanded him! And I myself was one of the five thousand he fed that day!' exclaimed the bystanders, hurrying to join the cheering crowd.

"Only the rulers, scowling in the background, were angry and afraid. Only Judas, walking so close, frowned bitterly as the procession came at last to the Temple, the greatest church in all the land. There Jesus dismounted, and went into his Father's house of prayer."

"And what about the donkey?" asked David John. "Did Jesus give him a pat, and did he get a nice cool drink before he trotted home again?"

"I expect so," smiled his mother, "and I'm sure he felt proud that he had done so well."

"So he went home to his mother," nodded David John, "and stood close beside her, like Duchess and her baby. Mother, will I ever have a ride on that little colt?"

"One day, when you're both older," said his mother, "perhaps you will."

AN END AND A BEGINNING

"WHAT's that nice smell?" shouted David John as he sniffed a warm spicy scent in the kitchen.

"Hot cross buns!" answered Susan. "We're having them because it's Good Friday."

"Boy! That's a good smell," David John said, "but why do we have them on—what did you say, Good Friday? What's Good Friday?"

"Don't you know that?" Susan asked. "In some countries people eat hot cross buns on Good Friday to remind them of the first Good Friday. Mother is making some for us. The icing on the bun makes a little cross and—"

"What's Good Friday?" David John asked again.

"It's—you tell him, Mother."

And Mother began the story. "On that Friday, nearly two thousand years ago, Jerusalem was crowded with people who had come to the city for the feast of the Passover. Everywhere people were talking about Jesus.

"Would he reign as king? The great men scowled as they listened to the talk for they feared and hated Jesus. Now, in the crowded city, riots might flare up at any moment if these foolish people really believed that the carpenter of Nazareth was to be king. If only the rulers could get rid of this Jesus! Yet they dare not arrest him publicly, for the people loved him. If only they could take him secretly—and soon! It was while they were plotting how to capture Jesus that the bitterness in Judas' heart overwhelmed him, and he knew what he was going to do. He would arrange to give Jesus up to his enemies."

"Oh, *no!*" cried David John. "He couldn't do *that!*"

"But he did," answered Mother. "Perhaps he said to himself, 'I will make Jesus show himself in his true colors. To save his own life, he will be forced to destroy his enemies,

like the mighty king I once thought him.' Jesus' enemies did not care what Judas thought. So long as they could arrest Jesus safely, they were willing to pay this traitor his thirty pieces of silver.

"While Jesus was sharing supper with his friends, the disciples, Judas slipped away into the night alone. The other friends did not notice. But Jesus knew that Judas had gone to betray him, and that death was very near. Now he had a great longing to be close to God, his Father. So he led his disciples out into the moonlight to the quiet garden of Gethsemane. There he went forward, and prayed to God alone, praying as even he had never prayed before.

"At last, with his heart at peace, Jesus came back to wake his sleeping disciples. They had scarcely stumbled to their feet when they heard voices, and saw the red flare of

torches among the dark trees. Out burst a crowd of people, armed with swords and clubs. At their head was Judas. 'The man I kiss is he—arrest him!' Judas whispered to some of the men of the mob.

" 'Master, Master!' Judas called, and kissed Jesus as though he loved him."

"How could Judas do it—how *could* he?" cried David John.

"As the dazed disciples suddenly realized their master's danger, Peter drew his sword and began to attack the whole mob. It was a wild and hopeless attempt—yet how could a man stand by and do nothing? But Jesus stepped forward quickly. 'Put away your sword,' he said firmly. 'If I wanted to escape, I could.' Then, turning to those who had come to capture him, he said, 'Let my friends go free!' And as they led him away, the terrified disciples fled."

"It was just like Jesus, to think of saving his friends," murmured Susan.

"Yes, even at a time like that," her mother agreed, "he thought of them.

"His enemies arranged to have Jesus put to death, to crucify him between two thieves, one on either side."

"Weren't any of his friends there with him?" asked David John.

"Only John was there," said Mother, "for the others had run away. But Mary, his mother, with some other faithful women, had come to be with her son to the end. Jesus had shown men how to live. Now he showed them how to die. Even now God was his Father. Even now he could not hate his enemies. They too were God's children, no matter how cruel and wrong they were.

" 'Father, forgive them,' Jesus prayed, 'for they know not what they do.'

"At last when Jesus felt that death was drawing near, he looked down and saw his mother weeping there, with John, the friend he loved so dearly, standing beside her. 'Mother,' he said, 'there is your son.' And to John he said, 'Look, John, there is your mother.' And from that day, John took Mary to his own home and cared for her as though she were his own mother.

"Now the time had come for Jesus to go home to God. 'Father,' he cried, 'I put my soul into your hands,' and then he died."

"Is that the end?" whispered David John after awhile.

"Oh, no," said his mother. "It was not the end but the beginning."

"For then came Easter Sunday!" interrupted Susan. "Tell us about that, Mother."

"They buried Jesus in a nearby garden in a tomb cut out of the rock," Mother went on. "His mother and Mary Magdalene watched the great round stone, as big as a cart wheel, rolled across the doorway to seal the tomb. Then, they walked slowly back to the city, stunned with grief.

"Early on the first day of the week, Mary Magdalene led two other faithful women back to the tomb. The city was silent and sleeping. There was no one in the quiet garden. As the sun rose they remembered the heavy stone across the doorway. 'Who will roll the stone away for us?'

93

they whispered anxiously as they hurried toward the tomb.

"Suddenly, Mary Magdalene, walking ahead, stared at the tomb and broke into a run. 'The stone has been moved!' she cried. 'Perhaps the body of Jesus has been stolen away.'

"Entering the tomb, they saw a young man sitting on the right side, dressed in a white robe. He said to them, 'Don't be frightened. You seek Jesus of Nazareth, who was crucified. He has risen, he is not here. Go tell his friends the disciples. . . .'

"Frightened and confused, the women turned and ran back through the city streets, where the early-risers stared at them. They ran to Jesus' friends. 'They have taken away the Lord,' gasped Mary, 'and we don't know where they have laid him!' "

"What did his friends do?" asked David John.

"At once John started to the tomb," Mother continued, "for he was young and quick and he knew the way. But when he saw that the stone had been moved, he stopped. Peter pushed past him and went straight inside. There was nothing there, nothing but the cloths they had wrapped around Jesus' body. Now John began to understand what had happened, but Peter didn't. Silently they walked slowly away. But Mary Magdalene, who had followed them to the tomb, stood weeping there.

"Suddenly, before her in the early morning light, there stood a man. 'Why are you crying?' he asked. *Perhaps this gardener at work so early would know what had happened,* thought Mary. 'Sir,' she begged, 'if you have taken him away, tell me where you have laid him.' But the man did

not answer her question. Instead, he spoke her name. 'Mary!' he said. Mary looked up and saw that it was Jesus himself. She flung herself at his feet, but Jesus said, 'Go and tell my friends, the disciples, that I am going to my Father and your Father; to my God and your God.'

"Speechless with joy and wonder, Mary raced back to tell the disciples. Now she understood. Jesus had risen from the dead! It was not the end, but a new beginning."

"Oh, I'm glad," said David John.

"So that's why Easter Sunday is such a happy day, isn't it, Mother?"

"Yes," nodded her mother, "because Jesus has not gone away from us. He is here with us all the time as he promised. 'I am with you *always*,' he said."

"That's good," said David John.

"Yes, that's very good," answered Mother. "A happy Easter to both of you, my dears."